# Curious George®

## Early Reader Collection

Houghton Mifflin Comp[...]
Boston 2008

D1021932

Copyright © 2008 by Universal Studios.  Curious George© and related characters, created
by Margret and H. A. Rey, are copyrighted and trademarked by Houghton Mifflin Company
and used under license. Curious George television series merchandise licensed by
Universal Studios Licensing LLLP. All rights reserved.

*Curious George® The Dog Show* copyright © 2006 by Universal Studios
*Curious George® Flies a Kite* copyright © 2006 by Universal Studios
*Curious George® Cleans Up* copyright © 2007 by Universal Studios
*Curious George® Plants a Seed* copyright © 2007 by Universal Studios
*Curious George® Roller Coaster* copyright © 2007 by Universal Studios
*Curious George® Takes a Trip* copyright © 2007 by Universal Studios

The PBS KIDS logo is a registered trademark of PBS and is used with permission.

For information about permission to reproduce selections from this book, write to
Permissions
Houghton Mifflin Company
215 Park Avenue South
New York, NY 10003

Special Markets ISBN: 978-0-547-17355-9

www.houghtonmifflinbooks.com

Printed in Singapore
TWP  10 9 8 7 6 5 4 3 2

# Contents

Curious George The Dog Show     1

Curious George The Kite     25

Curious George Cleans Up     49

Curious George Plants a Seed     73

Curious George Roller Coaster     97

Curious George Takes a Trip     121

# Curious George®
## The Dog Show

**Adaptation by Monica Perez**
**Based on the TV series teleplay written by Joe Fallon**

Houghton Mifflin Company
Boston

George was going to a dog show.

He had not been to a dog show before.

He was very curious.

The dog show was a surprise.
The dogs were not doing tricks.
They stood.

They walked.
They ran a little.
That was all.

George visited the dogs after the show.
It was much more fun.

George loved them so much that he
wanted to take them home.

So he did.
The dog owners were busy
getting ribbons.

They did not see George leave with their dogs.

At home George wanted to count
how many new friends he had.
It was hard work!
The dogs did not stay in one place.
George had an idea.

He put the big dogs in one room.
He put the small dogs in another room.

He put the hairy dogs in the bathroom.
Then he counted.
One . . . two . . . three hairy dogs.

One . . . two . . . three small dogs.

One . . . two . . . three big dogs.

The front door opened.
It was George's best friend.

The man was surprised to see dogs behind
every door.
"There must be twenty of them!" he said.

But George knew better.
There were three plus three
plus three dogs.
There were nine dogs in all.

The doorbell rang.
Nine dog owners had
come to get their dogs.

20

George waved goodbye
nine times.
What a great dog show it had been . . .
right in his own home.

**G**rouping numbers is an important math skill. Practice looking at everyday objects with your child and then counting them in different ways. For example, you can group rocks by size or color. Some ideas for counting and grouping: the trees on the playground, the clouds, cars, pens and pencils, pots and pans, and books.

# MATCH AND COUNT!

Counting by twos is often faster than counting each item if you have a lot of things to count. Match the socks below, circle each pair, and then count the pairs.

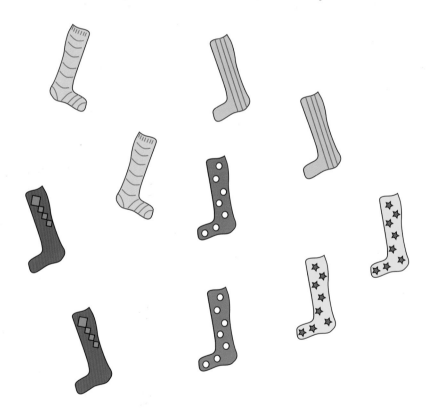

# 6 COLORFUL HATS!

Larger numbers are made up of smaller combinations of numbers. For example, two plus two is four, but three plus one is also four. Color hats in each row, count them, and fill in the blanks to get the same answer—six colorful hats!

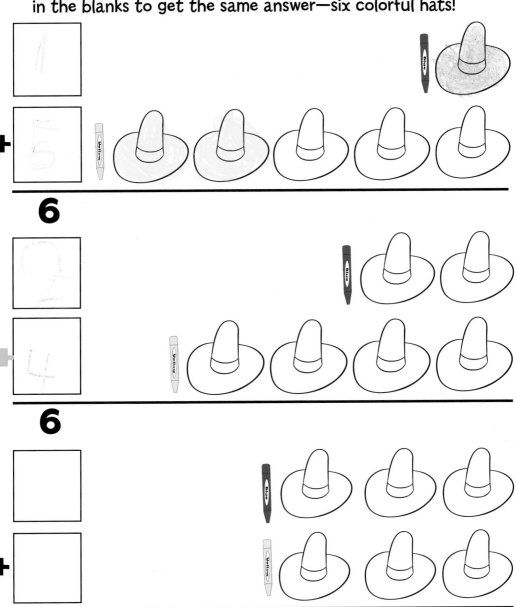

# COUNT THE ANIMALS

Is it hard to count all these animals? Try circling different animal groups and then adding the groups!

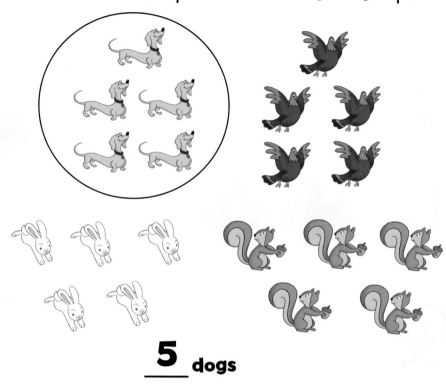

**5** dogs

+ _5_ pigeons

+ _5_ bunnies

+ _5_ squirrels

_____

_20_ **animals in all**

# Curious George®
## The Kite

**Adaptation by Monica Perez**
**Based on the TV series teleplay written by Joe Fallon**

Houghton Mifflin Company
Boston

It was a sunny day in the country.
George opened the window
to let in fresh cool air.

It was windy.

George liked to watch the wind
carry things away.

It carried leaves away.

It carried his cards away.

It did *not* carry his brick away.

As George looked up,
he saw something colorful in the sky.
It was a kite!

It belonged to Bill, the boy next door.
George wanted to fly the kite more
than anything in the world.

"Flying a kite is not easy," Bill said.

"But I can teach you."

Just then, his mom called,

"Billy, please come and help me!"

Bill gave George the kite string.

"Please watch my kite for me, George,"
he said. "I will be back soon."

George wanted to be good,
but he was also very curious.
He was curious about flying a kite.
George went to a field.
He held the kite up in the wind.
It began to fly away.

35

George chased the kite.

He chased it over a hill and past a farm.

The string pulled him along.

The wind was too strong.
It carried George away with the kite!

George was flying like a bird.
It was so much fun.
It was fun until George almost crashed
into a tree.

Now Jumpy the squirrel was flying too.
He did not like it.

Soon George was happy to see
the man with the yellow hat
flying nearby.
The man had a yellow hang glider.
He had come to take George
and Jumpy home.

George was glad to be on the
ground again.
He gave Bill the kite.
"Thanks. You are a great kite flyer!"
Bill said.
George liked flying,
but he liked walking more.

43

George still likes windy days.
He likes to fly kites.

He likes to fly kites that are
just the right size.

# BUILD IT YOURSELF!

### George likes to fly.
### Don't you?

# Here is how *you* can make a
# paper airplane of your own.

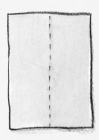

1. Fold a piece of paper in half the tall way, then unfold it again.

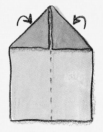

2. Fold down the top corners as shown in the picture.

3. Fold the edges in toward the crease you made in the middle.

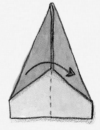

4. Now fold the plane in half and turn it to the side.

5. Make a wing from the front of the plane all the way to the back as shown in the picture.

6. You have a paper airplane!

# HIGH-FLYING FUN

## HOW TO FLY A KITE:

1. Fly on a day that's nicely windy. Check your local weather station—winds of 5-20 mph are best.

2. Face the direction the wind is blowing. Hold your kite straight up in the air and let the wind carry it aloft. Walk and let your line out to help the kite go higher.

3. If you have a friend with you, the friend can stand a few feet away from you and hold the kite. When your friend lets go, you can pull the string in slowly until your kite rises into the air.

4. When you're tired of flying, bring your kite down by reeling in the string and winding it around your kite spool.

**DON'T**

   . . . fly near telephone wires, trees, airports, or roads.
   . . . fly in rain or electrical storms.
   . . . forget to wear protective hand gear, like leather gloves.
   . . . fly near others.

**DO**

   . . . fly in an open field, as flat as possible.
   . . . take extra string, in case of mishaps.
   . . . add a colorful tail to your kite. It makes it easier to fly and looks
      great too.

## Have fun!

# Curious George®
## Cleans Up

**Adaptation by Stephen Krensky**
**Based on the TV series teleplay**
**written by Joe Fallon**

Houghton Mifflin Company
Boston

It was an exciting day.
A new rug had arrived.
George was curious to see
if it would fit.

It did!
George liked it.
It was the right color.

It was soft to walk on.
The rug was just perfect.

All that walking made George thirsty.
He poured himself a big glass of grape juice.

Then he went back to the rug.
It felt squishy between his toes.

George thought it would
be fun to jump on the rug.
So he jumped.

George forgot about
the grape juice.
It jumped, too.

What a mess!
George had to get that juice
off the rug.

He used paper towels first.
They did not work.

George remembered soap
was good for cleaning.
If one soap was good, many
soaps would be even better.

Now all George needed was water.

Maybe he used too much.

George went to
borrow a water
pump from a
nearby farm.

It was heavy, so he had
to put it on wheels.
And he had to get help
towing it home.

He used the pump a long time.
Finally there was more water
outside than inside.

When George was done, the rug was
cleaner than ever.

The whole room was cleaner, even if it was a little wet.

But it took a while for everything
to be perfect again.

# SIMPLE TOOLS AND TECHNOLOGY

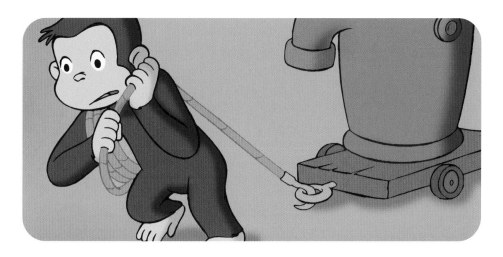

Curious George gets into trouble easily, but he always manages to find a way to fix things. In Cleans Up, he solves the problem with the help of a few simple tools. The pump was too heavy for him to lift or carry, so he used wheels and a rope for towing to help him reduce the pump's weight. What would you do in the following situation to help you solve the problem?

## THINK ABOUT IT

You have a very heavy box of books that you need to move across the room without carrying it in your arms the whole way. You have the following materials: a rope, a large, flat board of plywood, several plastic logs, and a helper. How would you do it? (See possible solutions below.)

1) You put the wood on the logs, and the box on the wood. As one of you pushes the box and board over the logs, the other keeps moving the last log to the front edge of the plywood to keep your board moving. 2) You tie the rope to the box and both of you pull it. 3) You move the books a few at a time! Are there any more solutions?

# HOW IT WORKS

Curious George used a water pump to get water from one place to another. The reason the water pump worked was because the pump created an area of low air pressure inside itself. The high pressure outside the pump pushed the water up to fill the area of low air pressure. Then the pump drained the water out its other end.

## HERE ARE TWO SIMPLE EXPERIMENTS WITH AIR PRESSURE

1. Stick a paper towel inside a jar and secure it with tape. Now fill your sink with water. Flip the jar upside down and plunge it into the water until it hits the bottom. Drain the sink. Did your paper towel get wet? Can you think why?

2. Insert a straw into a full glass of water. Place one finger over the top end and lift the straw out of the glass. Does the water fall out the bottom end? Now remove your finger. What happens to the water?

Explanations: 1) The air pressure inside the glass jar did not allow the water to enter the jar at all, keeping your paper towel dry. 2) When you held your finger over the straw, you lowered the air pressure on top of the straw. The higher air pressure at the bottom of the straw kept the water from falling out. Similarly, when you drink through a straw, you are not really sucking the liquid up. You are removing the air from the straw, lowering the pressure inside it. The greater air pressure outside the straw pushes water up into your mouth. It works just like George's pump!

# Curious George®
## Plants a Seed

Adaptation by Erica Zappy
Based on the TV series teleplay
written by Sandra Willard

Houghton Mifflin Company
Boston

Jumpy Squirrel was very busy.

George was curious.

What was Jumpy doing?

Bill, the boy next door, told George,
"Jumpy buries acorns and nuts.
He stores them in the ground.

He can dig them up later, when he is hungry."

That gave George
a great idea!
George buried the orange juice.
He buried the butter.
He buried the bread.
He was glad to find a
good place to store food.

When the man with the yellow hat came home, the kitchen was empty! Where was all of their food?

George proudly showed his friend.

"George, orange juice and bread are not for burying," the man with the yellow hat said. "They cannot be stored in the ground."

His friend showed George
a peanut with a sprout.
George was puzzled.

"This peanut grew into a plant,"
the man said. "Seeds and nuts
grow out of the ground, if they
are not eaten first."

George thought he understood.
If a little peanut could become a big
plant, what would a rubber band
become?

What would a feather become?

George dug lots
of holes.
He buried lots
of things.

Soon the house was empty.
The man with the yellow hat was
surprised!

"George, umbrellas and chairs are not for burying," the man with the yellow hat explained.
"They are made by people. They are not going to grow. Seeds and nuts will grow."

A few days later George saw
something new in the yard.
It was a sprout!
"Look, George," said his friend.
"A seed you buried is growing!
I wonder what it will be."

Soon there was a beautiful
sunflower in the yard.
George had a green
thumb after all!

# YOU CAN DO IT

GEORGE DISCOVERS THAT NOT EVERYTHING GROWS . . .
BUT SOME THINGS CERTAINLY DO!

If you'd like to grow something, try planting beans. In a few days, you'll have bean sprouts! You may need to ask a grownup for help with this exercise.

1. Fill a jar or plastic cup with half a cup of dried beans (a grownup can find these at the grocery store).

2. Cover them halfway with cool water.

3. Place a piece of nylon or cheesecloth on top of the cup and secure it with a rubber band.

4. Put it in a shady place for eight hours.

5. Gently drain the water through the cloth covering. Then add more water and immediately drain again.

6. Return the jar to the shady spot you found, but this time rest it on its side to give the beans more room to grow.

7. Rinse the beans twice a day for the next three days (as in step 5). After that, the sprouts will be ready to eat in a sandwich or salad! AND YOU GREW THEM YOURSELF!

# WATER TRAIL

If you'd like to know how water helps a plant grow strong, find a piece of celery and some food coloring — then you can see for yourself!

1. Ask a grownup to cut a single stalk of celery for you that still has the leaves attached to the top.

2. Pick a food coloring (red or blue works best) and add some drops of it to a full glass of water.

3. Put the celery, leaves at the top, in the glass of water and leave it in a sunny place.

4. In a few hours, you might notice something different about the celery. Wait overnight.

5. The next day, check out your celery. It will be colorful! Ask a grownup to cut the celery in half for you. You'll see colored dots inside the celery. This is how you know water travels from the bottom of the stalk up to the leaf — the same way it travels up the stem of a flower—to help the celery grow strong!

**Show what color your celery stalk became.**

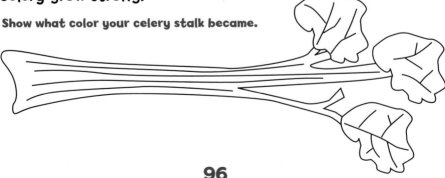

# Curious George®
## Roller Coaster

**Adaptation by Monica Perez**
**Based on the TV series teleplay**
**written by Lazar Saric**

Houghton Mifflin Company
Boston

George woke his friend up early.
Today was a special day.
They were going to Zany Island!

George was curious about riding the
roller coaster.
It was called the Turbo Python 3000.

It looked scary and fun.

Betsy and Steve had ridden it nine times!

They invited George to ride with them.

But there was a problem.

George was too short.

The man at the gate said George needed
to be five candy strings tall to ride.
George was only four.

How could George grow one candy
string in a day?

Maybe he could eat leaves like a giraffe.
Giraffes were tall.

Yuck!

The leaves tasted bad.

George took a bite of his candy string.

Candy tasted better.

What else could
he do to grow?
George thought exercising might help.
He lifted a heavy bar.

Then George measured himself.
He was now four and a half
candy strings tall!

George wondered if stretching
would make him grow.
He tried it.
By this time George was very tired.
He nibbled on his candy some more.

George saw a mother and baby.
The mother told the baby that sleep
would help him grow.
So George took a nap too.

When he woke,
he measured again.
Hooray! He was finally five candy
strings tall.

But the sign said he was still too
short to ride.
How could that be?

"Have you been biting your candy strings, George?" the man with the yellow hat asked.

George nodded.

"When the candy strings were longer, it took four to measure you," the man explained.

"Now that the candy strings are shorter, it takes more of them to measure you—five.

But you did not grow."

George was so disappointed.
Captain Zany, the park owner, walked by.
When he heard about George's
problem, he smiled.
"Since monkeys don't grow very tall,
we have a special sign for them."

Was George tall enough now?
You bet he was!

# HOW DOES IT MEASURE UP?

**Measuring tools you will need:**

**Empty paper towel roll**
**Empty toilet paper roll**
**Large paper clip**

Using each item in turn, measure the following distances. Fill in the chart with your measurements. Which distance was the largest? Did you get the same answer using all three methods of measurement?

|  | Paper Towel Roll | Toilet Paper Roll | Large Paper Clip |
|---|---|---|---|
| Length of your bed |  |  |  |
| Height of the kitchen table |  |  |  |
| Distance between your sofa and TV |  |  |  |

**Delving deeper:**

1. Which measuring tool was quickest to use?
2. Which measuring tool was most accurate (you did not have to estimate halves or "round up")?

Answers:

1. The paper towel roll would be quickest because it is the largest.

2. The paper clip would give the most accurate measurement. You would not have to "round up" much or at all. But it would be very hard to measure a very long distance with such a small instrument. The size of the object or the distance you measure can vary. This is why we use many different standards of measurement such as an inches, feet, yards, and miles.

# Chart Your Height

Start with a very long sheet of butcher paper or cut open some paper grocery bags and tape them together. Take a ruler or yardstick and draw a line down the edge of the longest side of the paper. Mark off inches all the way up the line.

Decorate your chart with paints, markers, crayons, or stickers.

Before you hang the chart on a wall, measure two feet up from the ground and mark the wall lightly with pencil. Leave this space empty. Place your chart so that its bottom is at the two-foot mark.

**5 feet** (60 inches)

54 inches

**4 feet** (48 inches)

42 inches

**3 feet** (36 inches)

30 inches

**2 feet** (24 inches)

Write "two feet" at the bottom of your chart and label every twelfth inch as three feet, four feet, five feet, etc.

Then stand against the chart and have a parent or friend mark your current height with pen or permanent ink on the chart. Label this line with the date and your age. Now when people ask, you can tell them exactly how tall you are!

Every six months, have someone mark your new height. You can probably use this chart for several years. When you are too tall for it, you can take it down, fold it up, and keep it as a record of how fast you grew.

# Curious George®

## Takes a Trip

Adaptation by Rotem Moscovich
Based on the TV series teleplay
written by Raye Lankford

Houghton Mifflin Company
Boston

Winter was long, cold, and snowy
in the big city.
George and the man with the
yellow hat were lucky . . .

They were going on vacation!
The suitcases were ready.
The tickets were ready.

George and his friend went to bed early.
Everything was set . . .

except the alarm clock!

"George! We overslept!" the man cried.

George and his friend dressed.

They dashed off to the airport.

"Hawaii, here we come!" the man said.

George was excited.

He had never been on an airplane before.

The man put the suitcases on a cart at
the airport.

"This will make them easier to carry,"
he said.

They rushed
to check in.
George climbed on top of the cart to
see over the ticket counter.

"Here is a gift for you," the ticket
clerk said.
She gave George a toy plane.
His first airplane!

George liked the airport already.

He flew his plane.

It landed on a red suitcase.

"Bad news," the man said.
"Our plane is late because of a big storm.
We have to sit and wait."
George did not mind waiting.

He had a brand-new toy.
But when George looked,
the toy was GONE!
The suitcase was gone!

Then George heard a beeping sound.

A motor cart drove by.

The red suitcase sat on top.

George ran after it.

The suitcase went faster.

George got on the moving sidewalk.

But he was going the wrong way!

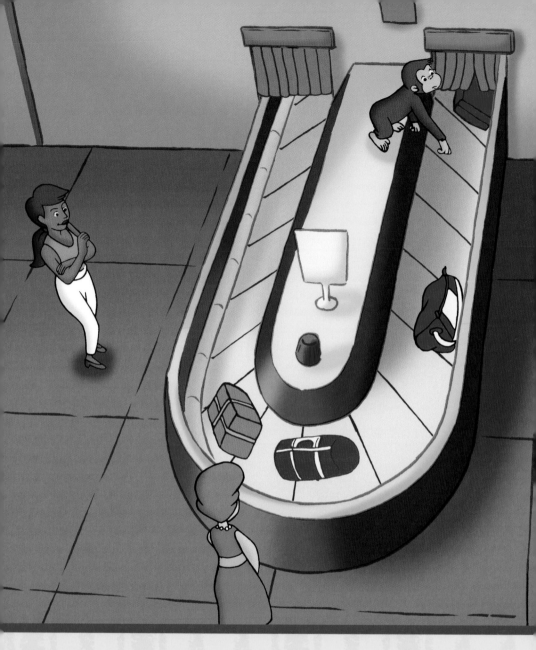

George heard a new noise.

Bags were moving on a long belt.

George spotted the red suitcase.

It was getting away.

George followed it.

He looked inside the suitcase.

No toy plane here.

Where should he look next?

Finally, the plane was ready.

But where was George?

"I cannot board the plane," the man said.

"I lost my monkey!"

"You mean George?"
the flight attendant asked.
She pointed at the plane.
George waved. He was on board already.

George and the man walked to their seats.

A nice woman stopped them.

"There you are! Did you lose this?" she said.

She gave George his toy plane.

That airport was a fun place!
There were so many different ways
to get around.
Maybe it was even better than vacation.

# TRAVELING
## Things and people get around in different ways.

Match the object or person with its mode of transportation.

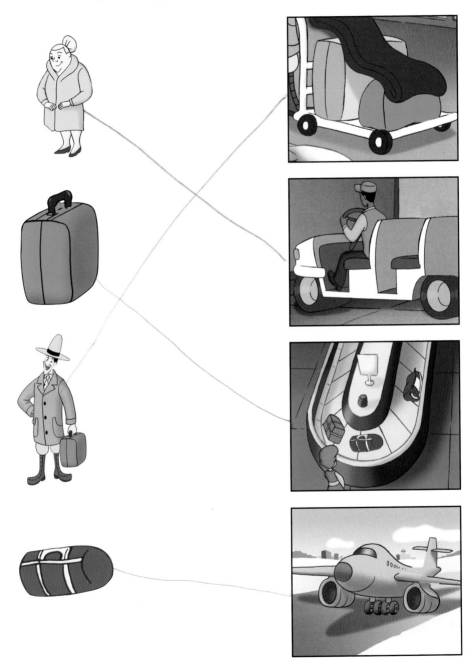

# ON THE GO!

## Balloon-Powered Train/Car:

You will need safety scissors, tape, a straw, a toy car or train, and a balloon.

1. Cut off the lip of the deflated balloon.
2. Cut the straw in half. Stick the straw into the balloon and tape it in place. Be sure to make a tight seal.
3. Tape the straw to the top of a car or train so the straw extends off the end.
4. Blow up the balloon using the straw and seal the balloon by pinching the straw's end.
5. Set the car down on a smooth surface and let it go.

## Getting There Is Half the Fun

A great way to take your own trip is to draw your destination and a "road map" to get there on a piece of butcher paper. Tear off a section as long as your table. Draw roads, buildings, and street signs. Now you can play with your small cars on your extra-large map!

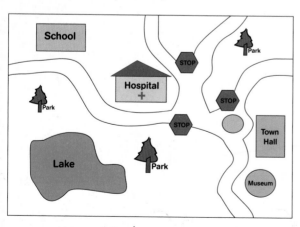